Harry Potter

AND THE HALF-BLOOD PRINCE

D0411040

Albus Dumbledore™,
Headmaster of Hogwarts™
and founder of the
Order of the Phoenix™

ALBUS DUMBLEDORE™ AND HARRY POTTER™

HOGWARTS
SCHOOL OF
WITCHCRAFT AND
WIZARDRY ™

Hogwarts

DRACO DORMIENS NUNQUAM TITILLANDUS

THE FOUR HOUSES OF HOGWARTS™
- GRYFFINDOR™, HUFFLEPUFF™,
SLYTHERIN™ AND RAVENCLAW™

HARRY POTTER™,
the Chosen One

Ginny Weasley™ and Harry Potter™

RON WEASLEY™

Ron Weasley™ and Hermione Granger™

Hermione Granger™

THE BEST WITCH
IN HER CLASS

HARRY AND HIS FRIENDS ARE UNITED IN THEIR FIGHT AGAINST VOLDEMORT™.

TRUE
FRIENDS

Ginny Weasley™

Molly and Arthur Weasley™

LUNA LOVEGOOD™

THE
QUIBBLER
PANDEMONIUM at THE MINISTRY
"WHAT A PALAVER!"
WRACKSPURTS
UNFUZZ THE MYSTERY PG12
EXCLUSIVE "MY WEEK WITHOUT RUNES!"
BY EDUAPHORA MERGUS
BREAKING NEWS
FISHWIVES FINALLY GRANTED EQUAL RIGHTS
LUNA LOVEGOOD'S FATHER IS EDITOR OF *THE QUIBBLER*™.

Lavender Brown™

LAVENDER BROWN
IS CRAZY ABOUT
RON WEASLEY™

R. WEASLEY 01

QUIDDITCH™

H. POTTER 07

GRYFFINDOR

G.
WEASLEY
05

Gryffindor ★★★

Captain

Seeker

GRYFFINDOR™

YOU CAN SCORE GRYFFINDOR!™

KEEPER

CHASER

TINCTURE No.3
Draught of Peace

FROM THE APOTHECARIUM OF
HORACE E. F. SLUGHORN

HORACE
SLUGHORN™,
Potions teacher

Slughorn holds parties for the members of his exclusive 'Slug Club'.

FELIX FELICIS™

NEW

ELECTRIC SHOCK SHAKE

WEASLEY & WEASLEY

Weasleys' WONDROUS ★Wands★

PROPER PRODUCT

WEASL

MAGIC JOKES!

Weasleys' WEATHER BOTTLE

Patent No. 483098 MADE IN ENGLAND

Weasleys' WONDROUS ★Wands★

TM & © Warner Bros. Entertainment Inc. (s09)

FRED AND GEORGE'S
SHOP IS IN
DIAGON ALLEY™.

MAGIC FUN!

Nymphadora Tonks™
and Remus Lupin™

DANGER
AT THE BURROW™

DEATH EATERS ATTACK

Bellatrix™
Lestrange

Death Eater™ Masks

Draco Malfoy™

ROOM OF REQUIREMENT™

SEVERUS SNAPE™ IS
THE HALF-BLOOD PRINCE™.

DARK SECRETS

PENUMBRA FOR ENEMIES

UNBREAKABLE VOW

The Unbreakable Vow™

CAUGHT

BY THE MINISTRY OF MAGIC

LUCIUS MALFOY™

CONSTANT VIGILANCE!

Azkaban Id/No. 51156

WANTED

BY THE MINISTRY OF MAGIC

BELLATRIX LESTRANGE

BELLATRIX LESTRANGE IS A KNOWN
CONVICTED MURDERER. FUGITIVE

★ APPROACH WITH

IF YOU HAVE AT
THIS PERSON
NEAR

WANTED

BY THE MINISTRY OF MAGIC

FENRIR GREYBACK™

FENRIR GREYBACK IS A SAVAGE WEREWOLF.
ONVICTED MURDERER. SUSPECTED DEATH EATER.

★ APPROACH WITH EXTREME CAUTION! ★

TOM RIDDLE™

The young
Voldemort

THE Dark LORD

He Who Must Not Be Named™

THE
SEARCH
FOR
HORCRUXES

THE PROPHECY

Neither Harry nor Voldemort can live while the other survives.

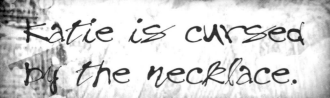
Katie is cursed by the necklace.

EXTREMELY POISONOUS

POTION N.86

CONTAINS POWDERED MOONSTONE & SYRUP OF HELLEBORE

№ 65487

L.150

EXTREMELY POISONOUS

POTION N.113

CONTAINS: JOBBERKNOLL FEATHERS & SYRUP OF ARNICA

№ 48765

EXTREMELY POISONOUS

POTION N.07

CONTAINS: ESSENCE OF VENOMOUS TENTACULAR & POWDERED LIONFISH

№ 66548

L.150

HARRY LOOKS FOR A BEZOAR IN SLUGHORN'S POTION KIT TO SAVE RON.

Voldemort

split his soul

into seven pieces.

Dumbledore
and Harry
travel to
the cave.

Dumbledore fights the Inferi.

BATTLE
ON
THE TOWER

A DARK TASK

A GREAT WIZARD